The Night LUNA's *Light* Went Out

K.J. FIELD

PlutoShine PRESS

FOR MY FAMILY, THE MOONS IN MY SKY.

BE LIKE THE MOON IN SOMEONE'S SKY AND SHOW HER THE WAY OF LIFE WITH YOUR LOVING SILVERY LIGHTS DURING THE DARKNESS.
— DEBASISH MRIDHA

DON'T WORRY IF YOU'RE MAKING WAVES JUST BY BEING YOURSELF. THE MOON DOES IT ALL THE TIME.
— SCOTT STABILE

First edition, October 2023.
ISBN 978-1-955815-15-4 Paperback
ISBN 978-1-955815-19-2 Ebook
ISBN 978-1-955815-17-8 Hardcover

Visit www.theplutodiaries.com/plutoshinepress   Find me on Twitter @Plutoliveshere

Earth and Luna were the best of friends. It had been that way since the early days of the solar system.

They traveled in the same circles.

Everywhere Earth went, Luna went, too.

Together they watched the humans
reach for the **STARS**.

They were **inseparable**.

Luna was the light of Earth's world.
Especially at night, when Luna came out to play.

Until one day... Luna got to thinking:

"Earth is a lot **BIGGER** than me."

It was the kind of thinking
that could only lead to one place:

A BIG BLACK HOLE

Before she knew it, Luna found herself
staring right into the center of it.

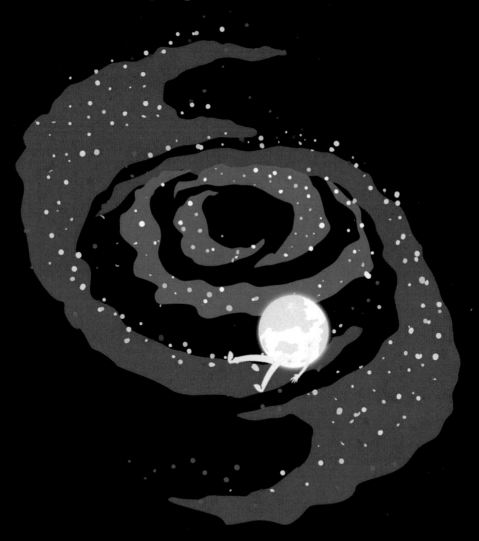

But the thoughts just kept on coming.

Earth had so many magnificent qualities!

Earth had C O L O R.

She had flowers that carpeted her meadows in sunny yellows, royal purples, and delicate pinks. She had lush gardens dressed in every shade of green imaginable.

She even had trees that changed
hue every couple of months,

from green

to red-orange

to white.

All she had to do was tilt a little to one side
as she spun her way around the Sun...
and the seasons just followed her lead!

Earth had **oceans**.
Not one, but **FIVE**, vast bodies of water
rippled across her surface!

In her tropical regions, she had delightfully warm water that teemed with vibrant sea life. And in her polar regions, she had refreshingly brisk water that ferried icebergs between snow banks.

Not only that, but Earth had something
no body else in the whole solar system had:

PEOPLE.

People who sang and danced in her lands.

People who raised their monuments to the sky.
People who engineered rockets and spacecraft.
People who explored worlds like *Earth* and *the Moon*.

Luna didn't have any of that.

No people to build things.

(Except for a few visitors Earth sent her,
all of whom left in a hurry.)

No meadows to dance in.

No water to flow across her surface.

And everywhere she looked, everything
was the **SAME** color: dusty *gray*.

There was no doubt about it: Earth was really going places!

Luna, it seemed, was just along for the ride.

And so one night, for the first time
in four billion years...

...Luna's light went out.

Then she slipped away into the darkness, far away fom Earth.

Nothing was the same without Luna's light.

Earthquakes rattled Earth's land and shook her to the core. The monuments people had built crumbled to the ground. All of Earth's creatures hid and trembled in the shadows.

Volcanoes spewed hot lava, ravaging her dewey meadows and seeping into her aquamarine oceans. Giant waves swept over her shores and then lay eerily still.

Earth's insides were **RIPPING** apart!

Without the pull of Luna's gravity
to hold her in place, Earth began
to tilt in new and dangerous ways.
Her beautiful seasons were no more.

Everything was wrong for Luna, too.

She had lost her best friend. Even worse,
she had hidden her face from the **SUN**.

It was the Sun that gave Luna the light she
reflected back onto Earth. Without the Sun's light,
Luna couldn't shine for *any* body, not even herself.

Away from the Sun's warm rays, Luna grew COLDER by the second.

She was ALONE.

Until a familiar voice broke through the silence:

"LUNA, PLEASE COME BACK!"

Reaching out into the darkness,
Luna felt the magnetic presence
of her old friend.

Earth drew her in close and gently turned
Luna's face toward the Sun once again.

In the soft glow of her new light, Luna could see things she had somehow missed before:

She had tall
mountains.

She had dark
patches that came
from ancient
lava flows.

She had **craters** with long rays
that resembled the Sun.

And she had moonbeams that shimmered a silvery gold as they brightened the paths of all Earth's creatures.

There was no doubt about it: Luna lit up Earth's night sky in a way *no* body else in the entire solar system ever could.

From the sky to the sea and beyond,
Earth and Luna made a magnificent team.

All About the Moon & Earth

The Moon doesn't make its own light -- only the sun and stars can do that! Moonlight is sunlight bouncing off the Moon's surface and onto Earth.

Earth reflects the sun's light, too. When Earth shines on the surface of the Moon, this light is called **earthshine**.

The Moon has many **craters**. These are bowl-shaped holes in the ground that were made when small space objects struck the surface.

The Moon's gravity pulls on the Earth, slowing down Earth's spin and keeping the planet tilted at a 25-degree angle.

The Moon's gravity also makes Earth's oceans bulge out. These bulges create the rise and fall in the sea surface, which we call **tides**.

What if the Moon Disappeared?

Ocean waves would be much weaker. Sea life whose survival depends on the strong movements of the tides would go extinct.

Animals that hunt at night wouldn't be able to see well. Many would not survive.

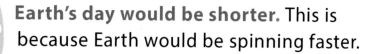

Earth's day would be shorter. This is because Earth would be spinning faster.

Earth's core could shift. This would set off natural disasters like earthquakes, volcanic eruptions, and tsunamis.

Earth could lose its tilt. Then there would be no seasons at all.

Earth could end up spinning on its side. Each half of the planet would have six months of daylight followed by six months of darkness.

If you enjoyed this book, would you kindly consider leaving a review? Reviews are tremendously important to an author's visibility in a crowded marketplace and help other readers find their next book. I look forward to reading your thoughts.
Thank you!

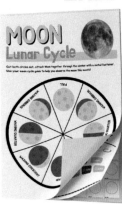
About the Author

KJ Field is an author, screenwriter, and space enthusiast who's been writing about the solar system since 2015. She has authored a number of space-themed fiction and nonfiction children's books, with many more on the way! KJ Field has been featured on BBC Radio Five Live for her expertise on dwarf planets. She is the voice of the Planet Pluto on X (Follow her @Plutoliveshere) and hopes to someday soon turn her screenplay about the plights and delights of a personified Pluto into an animated movie for all ages. To learn about new releases and special offers, please join her mailing list at theplutodiaries.com/plutoshinepress.

Want More Space Books for Kids?

Scan Me!

My First Book of Dwarf Planets: (nonfiction) *Get even the youngest space fan excited about the Big Universe of SMALL PLANETS! Through incredible space photos and easy-to-understand entries packed with fun facts, kids will get to know a fascinating lineup of dwarf planets: rocky Ceres; Pluto the planet with a heart; red Makemake, weird-and-wonderful Haumea; and icy, far-flung Eris. The most detailed book available for kids on our solar system's often-overlooked little planets! Made especially for ages 6-9.*
- Available Now!

5 Little Dwarf Planets: *A playful, science-packed introduction to Pluto and the dwarf planets told in sweet rhyming couplets. Introduce the solar system's five dwarf planets to children ages 3-8 with this fun planetary tale that proves small planets can shine just as bright as big ones. - Available Now!*

Jupiter the Gassy Giant: (picture book - *fiction/nonfiction blend*) *Jupiter loves his gassy surface. If only every body felt the same way! Moons Io and Ganymede are in for some aromatic surprises as they take a whiff of the Solar System's Gassiest Giant. But can two moons who don't know the joys of a gassy surface learn to appreciate the pungent aroma of their ginormous host planet? Take a deep dive into the scents of Jupiter with this adorable picture book as you enjoy a unique story approach to children's astronomy and chemistry.*
- Available Now!

Made in the USA
Monee, IL
06 December 2024

70966434R00026